THERE'LL ALWAYS
BE A
DRAYNEFLETE

THERE'LL ALWAYS BE A DRAYNEFLETE

BY
OSBERT LANCASTER

Illustrated by the Author

The Riverside Press, Cambridge
HOUGHTON MIFFLIN COMPANY BOSTON

CONTENTS

PREFACE

S o generally is the importance of local histories now realised that
an author need make no apology for adding to their number. It
was indeed a matter of some astonishment to discover that the
history of a town so well known as Drayneflete, with so rich and yet so
typical a past, should have been left so long unrecorded, and it was
therefore with some sense of mission that I set about my present task.

The local authorities, rightly anxious to stimulate the tourist trade
and fully intending that their town should play its proper role in the
forthcoming Festival of Britain, afforded every assistance and encour-
agement and I therefore welcome this opportunity of acknowledging
my indebtedness. In particular I should like to mention Miss Run-
corn, the Municipal Librarian, ever ready to transcribe original
documents in her keeping ; Mr. Soames, the learned and genial
curator of the Drayneflete museum and art gallery ; and Canon
Stavely-Locker and the Churchwardens of St. Ermintrude's, to whose
kindness I am indebted not only for permission to reproduce various
monuments in the Church, but for much curious and valuable
information.

Others without whose assistance this work could never have been
brought to a successful conclusion are Maud, Countess of Littlehampton, whose kind interest and charming sympathy added so much to the
pleasures of research ; Miss Dracula Parsley-ffigett, who proved a
veritable mine of extraordinary information which could have been
obtained from no other source ; the Hon. Mervyn Horder for so kindly
drawing my attention to the tune printed on page 14, of the existence
of which I should otherwise have remained totally unaware ; Mr.
John Piper for his advice on syntax ; and finally to my dear wife who
undertook the arduous task of proof-reading.

NOTES ON ILLUSTRATIONS

The illustrations on pp. 26, 59 are reproduced by kind permission of the Earl of Littlehampton : those on pp. 17, 21, 31, 32, 33, 42, 48 by kind permission of the Curator and Trustees of the Drayneflete Art Gallery : those on pp. 36, 40, by kind permission of Miss Dracula Parsley-ffigett. The reconstructions of historic Drayneflete were specially drawn for the present work and are founded on the results of the most recent archaeological research collated, in the later examples, with contemporary prints and photographs.

The design on the wrapper is reproduced from a hand-coloured engraving in the very rare 1721 edition of Tupman's *Pausanias Britannicus, or Albion's Beauties Newly Revealed,* and the wood-engraving of the old North Gate on the title-page is taken from *Picturesque Walks in Drayneflete and its Environs described by a Lady of Title* (London, 1852).

Few towns in England can boast so long a continuous history as Drayneflete. From the earliest times human habitations of one sort or another have clustered along the north bank of the River Drayne at the highest point where this shallow but treacherous stream is easily fordable. Or perhaps even earlier, for it is conceivable, though admittedly there is little to suggest it, that primitive man dwelt here before even there was a river at all, at a time when France and England were joined by a land-bridge and vast mammoths and sabre-toothed tigers prowled through the tropical undergrowth where now stands Marks and Spencers.

However that may be, we do know that early in the Bronze Age Drayneflete was already an important settlement on the great trackway from the Thames to the coast that has been known at various times as Wiggling Way, the Via Hernia and A 999. Interesting evidence of the high level of ' the Drayneflete culture ' (as it has come to be known) was afforded by the discovery of a long barrow some years ago during the rebuilding of the Fever Hospital on Drayneflete Down. Workmen, little realising the importance of their treasure-trove, unearthed some broken pots, a string of beads and a quantity of clay cylinders of undetermined purpose, all lying mingled with a quantity of human bones. The find was immediately recorded (see the *Proceedings of the Drayneflete Archaeological Society*, Volume XXXII, pp. 85–97), but it was not until the various objects had been submitted to the expert analysis of Professor Spiggot of London University and Dr. Flackenbacker of Yale, that their full significance was realised. For the layman it may seem almost incredible that so

Contents of a long barrow opened on Drayneflete Down in 1888, now in the Museum. From a drawing by Miss Catnip, published in the ' Proceedings of the Drayneflete Archaeological Society ', Vol. XXXII.

full a picture can be built up on so slight a foundation, but modern methods of laboratory research now enable archaeologists to speak with an assurance that would have astonished their predecessors. Lack of space prevents us from describing the complicated and laborious methods of enquiry employed by the Professors and we can only summarise their conclusions.

The occupant of the grave was, it appears, a local chieftain, middle-aged, five foot seven in height and markedly dolichocephalic. He was married, but not happy in his home life, suffered from stomach ulcers and an impacted wisdom tooth and died as a result of a sharp blow over the left ear. He had probably fallen on his head as a child and was certainly devoted to his dog, a cross-bred mastiff, eight hands in height with a badly damaged tail. The pottery was hand-turned of a fairly common type indicative of cultural contacts with the lower Meuse and probably did not hold water. The beads were imported from the Baltic and subject to a heavy purchase-tax which indicates that the Drayneflete community was comparatively wealthy. The clay cylinders of very peculiar shape were at one time thought to be primitive lace-bobbins, but as there is no evidence of lace-making at this early date Professor Flackenbacker is probably correct in saying that they played an important part in some fertility-rite.

The Romans, when they came, were not slow to realise the importance of the site and a large garrison town, Draconobododum, was soon established on the north bank. Innumerable discoveries made in the course of the huge-scale building development of the last twenty years have enabled us to form a fairly clear picture of the life and appearance of the town at this date, which would seem to have been of considerable size and importance. There was a temple of Castor and Pollux occupying the site of the present Parish Church, large baths situated roughly at the corner of the market square and Littlehampton Street, and another temple standing on ground now covered by the offices of the Drayneflete and District Electric Light Co., that was probably dedicated to the worship of Venus Suburbia, the Suburban Aphrodite, a cult very popular in Roman Britain. In the centre of the market square there stood a gigantic statue of an Emperor, of which the head (now in the Museum)

2

ROMAN DRAYNEFLETE

Gigantic head of an Emperor (Claudius? Caligula? Nero? Trojan? Vespasian?), discovered in 1885 in the Vicarage Garden, now in the Museum.

was discovered by a Mr. Brickworthy in 1885 when clearing out an old cesspool in the Vicarage garden.

In 1907 there were excavated the remains of a Roman villa at South Drayneflete which have been carefully preserved and can be viewed by the public on application to the custodian (Rosebud Cottage, Shinwell Lane). The plumbing arrangements, of great ingenuity and luxury, are well worth inspection and convey a very vivid idea of the high standard of living prevailing in the Roman Provinces in the second century A.D. There are also numerous fragments of mosaic pavements, including one of Leda and the Swan which is only shown to visitors on the production of a permit obtainable at the Town Hall.

Whether or not Christianity flourished in Roman Drayneflete is not clear, but we can hardly refuse to believe that there was a Christian community, small, doubtless, but correspondingly devout, established by the end of the second century. However, the theory, stoutly held by certain interested parties, that the Primitive Methodist Chapel in Station Road is built on the site of an early Christian basilica, has little evidence to support it and should be accepted with caution.

Exactly when, or why, the last Roman legions withdrew from Draconobododum we do not know, nor how soon after their departure the town fell a prey to marauding Saxons or Angles (or even possibly Jutes), but we do know, from the evidence provided by excavation, that the town was completely destroyed by fire, probably early in the fifth century.

The first literary mention of Drayneflete occurs in the Chronicle

4

at a date about a century later than the sack. According to the monkish chronicler it was at Drayneflete that Filthfroth the Brisling was baptised together with all his house-carls by St. Eggfrith, an event that is charmingly commemorated in the north aisle of the present church by a stained-glass window, the work of Sir Edwin Burne-Jones, presented in 1898 by Miss Wicker in memory of her brother Colonel Wicker who fell in the second Zulu War. The actual circumstances of the conversion of this powerful ruler are the subject of a delightful legend which gained for the town an enviable reputation as a place of pilgrimage throughout the Middle Ages.

Filthfroth, say the chroniclers, was passing through the town on his way to raid the men of Wessex, and, being very tired, decided to pass the night in the great hall of the local thane. Now it so happened that in the household of this thane was a little girl who, quite unknown to her parents, was already a Christian. No sooner had the whole of Filthfroth's household lain down to sleep, than the small child started to recite the 119th Psalm. Now in those days, of course, there were no separate bedrooms and the whole household and all the travellers were passing the night on the floor of the Great Hall. This circumstance naturally rendered the little convert's devotions rather disturbing for her companions and when she had finally come to the end of her song of praise only immediately to start again at the beginning, Filthfroth angrily demanded that she should be immediately silenced. This, however, proved to be easier said than done : in vain was the determined child ordered, entreated, threatened, bullied and finally beaten. Still her little voice rang out. At last, at three o'clock in the morning she revealed that her tongue could only be stilled by the immediate baptism of the Brisling and all his household. Accordingly a message was at once sent to St. Eggfrith, who fortunately was dwelling in a hermitage close by, and just as dawn was breaking Filthfroth, the thane and all their followers were received into the Church, whereupon the little missionary, worn out by her efforts, immediately expired. So moved were the whole company by this event that Filthfroth then and there commanded that a church should be built which was consecrated less than a year later, and where beneath the High Altar the bones of little St. Ermintrude, for such was the child's name, were piously interred.

5

Of this Saxon church virtually nothing remains today, although it is possible that the traces of long-and-short work at the base of the tower may have survived from this date, but in the churchyard there stood (until 1910 when it was removed to the Museum) the broken shaft of a Saxon cross that may well have been contemporary with St. Ermintrude's church. The decoration of this monument is of peculiar interest as exhibiting a mingling of classical and Scandinavian motifs unique at this date and has been made the subject of a monograph by Professor Hjalmar Hjalmarsen of Upsala published in the *Jahrbuch für frühchristliche Kunstwissenschaft.*

Saxon cross formerly in the churchyard, now in Museum.

Apart from the cross the only other remains of Saxon Drayneflete are a collection of coins, pots, two broken sword shafts, and a copper dish, probably of Byzantine workmanship, engraved with a view of a domed building, possibly St. Sophia, and bearing the legend A PRESENT FROM CONSTANTINOPLE in Greek, which was discovered on the sewage farm some years ago and is known as the 'Drayneflete Hoard'.

However, we should not assume from the comparative paucity of the existing evidence, that Drayneflete was a place of small importance in Saxon times. On the contrary contemporary references, though few, all point to its being a flourishing centre of commerce and religion, and we know that at least one Anglo-Saxon monarch,

6

Ethelred the Unready, held his court Moot in the town on two separate occasions. Moreover, late in the ninth century it was the scene of important ecclesiastical events when the Synod of Drayneflete was held in the Church : the Synod at which, it will be recalled, the vexed question of whether or not deacons should be allowed to wear beards without moustaches was finally decided, not, alas, without bloodshed, in favour of Bishop Bolfric and the compulsory moustaches party.

A very few years after these important events, the whole town was destroyed by the Vikings who, under the command of Old Ekdal (or the Wild Duck as he was sometimes called after the device at his masthead) sailed up the Drayne, burnt the church and put all the inhabitants to the sword. Recovery after this disaster was slow, and Drayneflete had not long risen from her ashes when Norman William overthrew Saxon Harold and ushered in the Middle Ages.

Drayneflete Canonicorum

The development of Drayneflete during the Middle Ages was inseparably bound up with that of the institutions of the Church, and the most prominent remaining monuments of this age are all, as elsewhere, ecclesiastical. At the time of the Conquest there already existed a stone-built church, dedicated, curiously enough, to St. Sorbo, a saint of whom virtually nothing is known, but whose name has been thought by some to indicate a Celtic origin, while others have attempted to identify him (or her) with St. Sambo, a holy man alleged to have been popular in Asia Minor in the first century and traditionally held to have been the Ethiopian eunuch baptised by St. Philip. This church which had replaced the one built by Filthfroth (probably destroyed in Viking raids) was itself superseded by a new structure in the Norman style erected towards the end of the eleventh century. All that now remains of the pre-Conquest shrine is the base of the west tower and one Saxon window of two lights of rude and primitive workmanship. The Norman church consisted of a single aisle and a chancel with a rounded apse. At the very end of the thirteenth century a further rebuilding took place : the south wall was pierced to form an arcade of pointed arches rising on clustered shafts giving on to the new aisle, and the chancel was rebuilt in its present

An interesting old corbel (late-fourteenth century) in the south aisle of the Parish Church.

form with an east window of three pointed lancets. A little more than a century later new windows in a style midway between Decorated and Perpendicular were inserted in the south aisle and shortly afterwards a further two stories were added to the tower which, when completed, with an openwork balustrade and pinnacles in the Perpendicular style, must have made a very striking addition

9

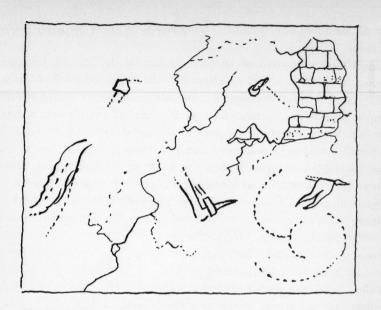

A fifteenth-century wall-painting of St. George over the arcading of the north aisle of the Parish Church. The first plate shows the state of the painting at the time of its accidental discovery during repairs to bomb damage in 1944; the second, after a tactful cleaning by Professor Isolde.

to all views of the town. Unfortunately 'Lord Littlehampton's Stump', as it was popularly called locally, did not long survive, being totally destroyed in the great storm of 1608. The beautiful south porch, which happily still exists, dates from a few years later. After the close of the Middle Ages one further addition was made to the church in the shape of the north aisle erected by Sir Pompey Fidgett to accommodate his family tombs in the debased and degraded Gothic of the early seventeenth century. Of the inspired restoration carried out by Sir Gilbert Scott, when many hideous eighteenth-century additions were removed and the whole fabric regained its pristine beauty, I shall speak in the proper place.

The parish church, however, was neither the sole nor the most prominent ecclesiastical building in the town. Late in the thirteenth century a house of Augustinian Canons was established on the banks of the Drayne just outside the North Gate, which continued to flourish and expand up to the time of the Dissolution. Today, alas, all that remains is the exquisite Gateway at the north-east corner of the Market Place known as Prior Bloodwort's Lodging, with its great panelled solar above the archway, now occupied by the offices of the Regional Petroleum Officer. Prior Bloodwort, of whom a life-like statue, now in the Museum, stood in the niche to the west of the arch until it was removed to make way for the present traffic-lights in 1935, played a prominent role in the local history. On traditionally bad terms with the townsmen he gained their undying hatred by appropriating, in addition to the rights of ullage, socage and *jus primae noctis* (exercised, naturally, by a lay deputy), the tolls on the bridge over the River Drayne. Against this unwarrantable extension of the Church's claims the townspeople long protested in vain, and it was not until they were in a position to inform against him to the High Sheriff that he was eventually undone. Unfortunately for him he was unable to answer charges that he had illegally suppressed a prosecution for short-weight baking against a local firm in return for a consideration, and although it was never proved that he received any more than a pork-pasty and half a bottle of sack, he was removed from his office by the Chancellor of the Diocese.

Prior Bloodwort's Lodging, although the sole architectural, is not

FIFTEENTH-CENTURY DRAYNEFLETE

the only remaining treasure of Drayneflete Abbey. Better known, by far, is the delightful Drayneflete Carol, composed by an anonymous member of the community in the early fourteenth century, and now preserved in the British Museum (Drayneflete MSS. No. 6089–10–11) which was first sung on the occasion of a Yuletide visit to Drayneflete of the young Richard II. Although it has already been the subject of twenty-one talks in the Third Programme by Professor Harpsbaum, I print it here in full for the benefit of such readers who may still be unacquainted with this exquisite gem of Middle English prosody.

Alle littel childer syng
Prayses to our yonge Kyng
Some syng sherpe and some syng flat
Alma Mater Exeat.

Alle engels in ye skie
Maken loude melodie
With sackbut, organ, pipe and drum
Ad Terrorem Omnium.

Ye povre beastes in ye stalle,
Alack, they cannot syng at alle
Ne cock ne henne of either sexe
De Minimis Non Curat Lex.*

Although apart from the Prior's Lodging no traces of Drayneflete Priory exist today, two subsidiary establishments have happily survived. One is the Chapel of St. Bodeswide standing on the quayside immediately behind the Town Hall, which was erected at the same time as the first stone bridge over the Drayne, and is now occupied

---

* The earliest known tune attached to this carol is generally attributed to Myrffyn ap Hwdda who was beaten to death with a lyre by a rival competitor at a late sixteenth-century Eisteddfod.

by the County Food Office : the other is the ruined chapel of the Augustinians in the Littlehampton Memorial Park that received very rough treatment at the hands of ' the Gothicising improvers ' responsible for laying out the park in the late eighteenth century, and has recently been incorporated into the People's Self-Service Refreshment Room and Cafeteria which was opened by the municipality last summer.

Of the secular remains of medieval Drayneflete virtually nothing remains. Gone is the exquisite old Custard Cross where the market price of custards (or costards) was regularly fixed by the master of the Custard Makers' Guild, and the memory of it survives only in a few rare seventeenth-century engravings ; gone is the beautiful old Moot Hall, wantonly destroyed at the end of the seventeenth century to make way for a heavy and ill-proportioned building in the Renaissance style ; gone the fine fourteenth-century hall of the Worshipful Company of Drumstretchers. Of the town walls, still standing in the eighteenth century, there remain a few traces of medieval masonry at the back of the cinema, miraculously laid bare by aerial bombardment and now carefully preserved ; but of the wonderful old North

Master Humfrey Figet. From a memorial brass in the Parish Church.

15

Gate, represented in many old prints, not one stone remains upon another.

Of all the treasures of medieval Drayneflete, that of which the disappearance is to be, perhaps, most deeply regretted, is the old Fidget House, a miracle of half-timbering and carved newel-posts which stood, until well into the eighteenth century, up against the Prior's Lodging.

The remarkable family of Fidget, or ffigett, can boast a longer connection with the town than any other. The first Figet (or Fidget) of whom we have any record is Master Humfrey Figet whose effigy in brass lies in the south aisle of the Parish Church. The old theory that he was the son of a pawnbroker and ' contact man ' for Prior Bloodwort has long since been disproved by the researches of the late Miss Dracula Parsley-ffigett who has conclusively shown that he came of a very ancient Welsh family of gentle birth. By the middle of the fifteenth century he was already the most prominent local citizen, being Master of the Custard Makers, twice Mayor and finally for a short time High Sheriff of the County. However, the great days of the family date from the time of the Dissolution of the Monasteries, when Master Humfrey's grandson Sir Jonas Fidget received a grant of Drayneflete Priory from the King, and must be left for further consideration in the next chapter.

The most important result of the reform of religion in Drayneflete was the disappearance of the Priory and the erection on its site (and with much of its materials) of the magnificent Tudor mansion of the Fidgets, happily still standing on the banks of the

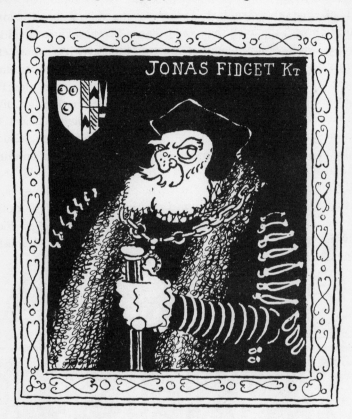

Sir Jonas Fidget. From a portrait by an unknown artist now in the Art Gallery.

Drayne. A sincere friend of the reformed faith, except for a short period under Queen Mary, Sir Jonas Fidget played no small role in the glorious history of his times. Although he took no active part in the many voyages and explorations which rendered memorable

17

the reign of the Virgin Queen, by financing, at a very reasonable rate of interest, numerous contemporary expeditions, he is entitled to a full share in the triumphs and glories of this great period of English History. With the cultural and artistic life of his time, his connection is less well-established. Tradition maintains that he is the original of the character Master Bloody, the miser, in the old play *Gaffer Gerkins Pryck* (attributed variously to Massinger, Beaumont, Fletcher, Greene and Kyd), and as a Justice of the Peace he sentenced a large number of contemporary poets and pamphleteers to have their ears cropped. Of his charitable and philanthropic activities, however, a concrete memorial remains in the shape of the Fidget Almshouses in the Station Road, and the school for poor scholars which originally stood hard by the bridge but which was transferred in the last century to the magnificent new building by Mr. Waterhouse on Drayneflete Down. Dying at a very advanced age, ' from a surfeit of apricocks ' according to the chronicler of the time, he was succeeded by his son, Sir Pompey Fidget.

Sir Pompey Fidget ;   the effigy on his tomb in the Fidget Chapel in the Parish Church.

18

Sir Pompey, the first baronet, had a distinguished military career in the Low Countries, where he trailed a pike in the Field Security Police, and was responsible for the apprehension of many dangerous characters in our ranks suspected of half-hearted acceptance of the Thirty-nine Articles or of communicating with the Jesuits. For his loyal services he was created a baronet and privileged to entertain his Sovereign at Fidget Priory, an honour which cost him almost as much as he had made out of the confiscations imposed on the traitors whom he had denounced. He was four times married, and lies beneath a handsome monument in the chapel which he added to the Parish Church. This effigy, which is a very fine example of contemporary sculpture, gains an added interest from the presence of his faithful hound, a feature which Mrs. Esdaile regards as almost unique at this period and which makes the monument very popular with visitors, many of whom have signed their names in indelible pencil on the animal's hind quarters. Of his numerous offspring the most notable was his third son, Hezekiah, who left his native country during the last part of King James's reign, after a series of unfortunate financial reverses, for the New World, where he founded the town of Drayneflete, New Hampshire, and where his family is today worthily represented by Senator Wilbur P. Fidgett V.

Of the other Drayneflete worthies of the seventeenth century the most illustrious was probably that strange character, Dr. Ezekiel Peppercorn, who is today best remembered for his discovery of the medicinal properties of the lesser bindweed, and his ingenious, though never-realised, project for a silent flush. In his own day his fame largely rested on his great work, *Hydrophilie or the Properties of the Fourth Element Explained, to which is appended an exact account of the marvellous great Privy in King Solomon's Temple.* He it was who was responsible for the notorious Drayneflete Water Riots in 1632. On this occasion a handsome new pump, the gift to the town of Sir Jeremy Fidget, who had long been anxious to provide his fellow citizens with a purer supply of drinking-water than that afforded by the River Drayne, was totally demolished by an angry mob inflamed by the eloquence of Dr. Peppercorn who had preached for two and a half hours on the text ' Are not Abana and Pharpar, rivers of Damascus, better than all the waters of Israel ? ' This remarkable character, who lived for

The memorial to Dr. Peppercorn in the chancel of the Parish Church.

fifty-six years in a house still standing, in Pump Court, finally died of a dropsy in his eightieth year and was buried in the church. In 1925 a memorial plaque was placed on No. 2 Pump Court by the Municipality and unveiled by the Chairman of the Metropolitan Water Board.

The seventeenth century was perhaps, anyhow in Drayneflete, richer in personalities than in monuments. The most noteworthy addition to the town during this period was the old Town Hall, a high-roofed classical structure, that was erected on the site of the Moot Hall in 1675. It was replaced by the present building in 1881, unregretted by all who knew it. The old Custard Cross had been wantonly pulled down some years earlier, on the specious plea that its style of ornament was Papist and that the shelter it afforded was conducive to immorality on wet Sunday afternoons.

Still stranger, perhaps, than their disregard of the claims of antiquity was the seventeenth-century public's unawareness of the true beauty of their own buildings; thus many of the fine old half-timbered houses erected during this period were covered by a flat wash of common plaster. Fortunately, more enlightened ideas prevail today and the Council has been at great pains to strip off this outer covering on such houses of that date as have now survived, thus revealing for the first time the full beauty of the glorious old oak beams.

Drayneflete : a general view of the town in the mid-seventeenth century from a painting by the younger Truyp, formerly in the Littlehampton collection, now in the Art Gallery.

The most remarkable of the existing buildings of this period is undoubtedly the *King's Head* Inn in the Market Place. It is known that an alehouse had stood on this site from very early times, but no part of the present structure, which has undergone numerous alterations in the intervening years, is older than the mid-seventeenth century. Of the distinguished travellers who have from time to time lain beneath its hospitable roof the name is legion. Although there is no mention of it in his diary, there is a firm tradition that Samuel Pepys frequently stopped here on his way to Dover and one of the

DRAYNEFLETE AT THE END OF THE SEVENTEENTH CENTURY

The sepulchral monument of the fifth Viscount Littlehampton in the Parish Church.

bedrooms still bears his name. Likewise it has long been believed that it was at the *King's Head* that General Wolfe spent his last night in England and a copy of Gray's *Elegy* which he is said to have left behind is still preserved in the Smoking Room. (Albeit as it is the 1810 edition it is just possible that the general's own copy may perhaps have been purloined at some period and a substitution effected.)

Of considerable importance to the life and development of the town at this date was the arrival of the fourth Lord Littlehampton at Drayneflete Castle. This massive pile, which had been erected on the west bank of the Drayne shortly after the Conquest, had remained in the possession of the de Cowgumber family until the extinction of the male line on the execution of Sir Thomas de Cowgumber, his cousin Lord Cowgumber and his five brothers on Tower Hill in 1533. It then passed through the female line into the family of Lord Little-hampton who continued, however, to reside on their old Sussex estate at Courantsdair.

In 1672, however, the then Lord Littlehampton (the ' Wicked Lord ') decided to leave his castle at Courantsdair and reside at Drayneflete, whence he could more easily reach his town house in Covent Garden. He at once set about improving his property and planned a mansion that was to rival in size Castle Howard or Seaton Delaval. Unfortunately funds ran out and only the central block was ever finished which must, adjacent to the still standing medieval ruins, have presented a very bizarre appearance. On his death in 1679 he was buried in the Parish Church where a magnificent marble monument, the work of an as yet unidentified sculptor, testifies to his virtues. The clustered banners and drums in the background recall the martial qualities of the deceased which were chiefly revealed during his tenure of the Office of Master of the Ordinance, a post he occupied during a short period of unbroken peace.

The eighteenth century at Drayneflete was a time of rapid expansion during which the appearance of the town was considerably modified. Many of the splendid old timber houses were ruthlessly torn down and replaced by the square brick boxes which were the century's principal contribution to domestic architecture. Among the more elaborate buildings of this period should be noted the Corn

25

The second Earl of Littlehampton ('Sensibility Littlehampton'). From a portrait by
Pompeo Battoni, painted in Rome in 1769, in the collection of the present Earl.

Exchange in Market Street, half of which is still fortunately standing alongside Messrs. Pixol's new show-rooms ; the old Rectory, a fine red-brick mansion in the style of Sir Christopher Wren just behind the Church, which now houses the Drayneflete Museum and Art Gallery (*Open every day from ten till four. Entrance 6d. Special terms for schools.*) and an equestrian statue of William of Orange removed in 1897, to make way for the statue of Queen Victoria, to a new site behind the Town Hall.

The greatest of the many illustrious figures connected with Drayneflete during the period was undoubtedly Alexander, second Earl and eleventh Baron Littlehampton, the grandson of the 'Wicked Lord'. A man of wide culture and great sensibility, he devoted himself throughout a long life to the promotion of literature and the arts. The splendid collection of pictures that he formed has rendered his name familiar to all lovers of painting and his enlightened patronage supported numerous poets, architects and landscape-gardeners during their struggling years, and in some cases long after they had ceased to struggle. In his lifetime Drayneflete castle was twice completely rebuilt, first in the Palladian and then in the Gothic style. He it was who was responsible for ' Lord Littlehampton's Folly ', an architectural curiosity expressly designed to display correct examples of all the five great schools of architecture. On ground level was a square pavilion from the façades of which projected classical porticos, in the Ionic, Doric, Corinthian and Tuscan orders respectively, adorned with numerous busts of Vitruvius, Palladio, Inigo Jones and other worthies. On this rested a Gothic octagon, pierced with traceried windows and sustained by flying buttresses, supporting a three-storied Chinese pagoda, that terminated in a cupola in the Hindoo taste. Under the whole structure was an Egyptian crypt. Completed in 1799, this curious freak remained intact until the night of its noble builder's death, when the oriental or uppermost sections were struck by lightning at the very hour when Lord Littlehampton was breathing his last. The Gothic octagon survived until 1923, when it was removed as being unsafe ; while the classical pavilion on the ground floor remained comparatively intact until it was taken over by an A.A. battery as living-quarters for the A.T.S. in 1941. Today all that remains is the Egyptian crypt which rendered yeoman service as an

27

Lord Littlehampton's Folly

air-raid shelter for the inmates of the County Lunatic Asylum through-out the ' blitz '.

The best known of the numerous cultured figures who formed the Littlehampton circle was the poet Jeremy Tipple, but of him I shall speak at greater length when we come to consider the suburban development of the town.

Hardly less illustrious, however, was Dr. Palinure, the celebrated Bishop of Horizon and the Isles. Born of humble Protestant stock on Lord Littlehampton's Irish estates at Spanielstown, his early promise soon attracted his Lordship's notice, and at his expense he was able to go first to Trinity College, Dublin, and later to Oxford. On leaving the University he became Personal Chaplain to his patron, who presented him with the living of Drayneflete at the first oppor-tunity ; to this were added in the course of time the livings of Belching-cum-Sowerby, Blicester, Great Danehampton, Toad-in-the-Wold, St. Ursula-inside-the-Wardrobe and Stobdalkin in Co. Meath. As the years passed and his fame grew he became Canon of Christ Church, Archdeacon of Bloomsbury, Dean of Spanielstown, Chaplain-out-of-the-Ordinary to his Majesty, and finally Bishop of Horizon and the Isles. Today these distinctions are largely forgotten but he lives in the memory of all as the author of that exquisite hymn (No. 882, Hymns Ancient and Modern) which starts :

> How little, Lord, we need below
> As through this vale of tears we go.
> He doth all worldly goods despise,
> Who striveth for a heavenly prize.

Although few of his contemporaries enjoyed a greater reputation for learning, apart from the above-quoted hymn, his published works were confined to a volume of sermons and some translations of Ovid. The scantiness of literary remains should not blind us, however, to the real importance of the influence he exercised, supported by his wit and conversation, in contemporary thought and letters. In early life he was regarded as the principal interpreter of the ideas of the Encyclopaedists to the English public, a role he successfully sustained although almost totally ignorant of the French language, and by the more orthodox was looked on as a convinced Latitudinarian, if not a

29

JOHANNES JACOBUS PALINURE, ARMIGER.
EPISCOPUS HORIZONIS INSULARUMQUE.
All worldly goods he doth despise
Who striveth for the heavenly prize.
ERECTED BY PUBLIC SUBSCRIPTION ANNO. DOM. MDCCCXXXIII.

The memorial to Dr. Palinure by a pupil of Flaxman in the Parish Church.

Deist. Later, however, when the French Revolution had made clear the terrible consequences of loose thinking, he rallied strongly in support of Church and State, and in his later years no one was more outspoken in his condemnation of all enthusiasm, and both Tractarians and Evangelicals had good cause to beware of the sharpness of his tongue. But despite the firmness of his convictions he was by no means an austere or unapproachable man : he kept the best table of all the bench of Bishops and left behind him in manuscript a collection

30

of 128 different recipes for cooking trout.   He was, moreover, the
first clergyman ever to become a member of White's Club.   He died
full of years and honour in 1832 largely as a result of the exceptional
exertion occasioned by his coming up to London when in a poor state
of health, solely in order to deliver an unforgettable attack on the

*Sir Toby Fidget by Kneller.   A portrait now in the Art
Gallery.*

Reform Bill in the House of Lords.   He died in his town house in
Bloomsbury, but in accordance with his oft-expressed desire, he was
buried at Drayneflete, where a fine marble monument to his memory,
the work of a pupil of Flaxman, was erected by public subscription in
the south aisle of the Parish Church.

Thanks to the establishment of Lord Littlehampton at Drayneflete Castle the prominence of the Fidgetts was a little reduced during
this period, although their wealth increased and their social importance
was considerably reinforced by the marriage of Sir Toby Fidgett, the
grandson of Sir Pompey, with the eldest daughter of the 'Wicked

' La Belle Fidgett ' by Lely. A portrait now in the Art Gallery.

Lord Littlehampton '. This lady, renowned for her beauty and high
spirits, was known in Court circles, in which she passed much of her
time, as ' La Belle Fidgett '. Her husband, a more placid type,
devoted himself exclusively to the cultivation of tulips and the per-
fection of a gigantic water-clock that was still unfinished at his death.
Their eldest son, Sir Hercules Fidgett, was a noted sportsman, whose
prowess in the hunting-field is still recalled in the Drayneflete country.
His married life was not, alas, very happy ; his wife, never being able

32

Sir Hercules Fidget by Stubbs.   A painting now in the Art Gallery.

to accustom herself to his lifelong habit of kennelling twenty or more hounds in the bedroom, finally ran off with the Master of an East Indiaman.   However, these were but passing clouds temporarily obscuring the lustre of the house of Fidgett, and in the next chapter we shall see how its greatest triumphs were reserved for the nineteenth century.

DRAYNEFLETE EARLY IN THE NINETEENTH CENTURY

I n Drayneflete, no less than elsewhere, the nineteenth century was a period of rapid expansion and long-needed improvement. Up to the accession of Queen Victoria the pace was slow, but after this happy event the rate of renovation and addition was much accelerated. This was, perhaps, less directly due to any personal influence that the young sovereign may have exercised on the course

Sir Jonas Fidgett. From a daguerreotype, formerly in the possession of Miss Amelia Parsley-ffidget.

of local events than to the personality and far-sighted enterprise of that great philanthropist and worthy son of Drayneflete, Sir Jonas Fidgett. Sir Jonas, who succeeded his grandfather Sir Hercules, as fifth baronet while still a child, displayed on reaching years of discretion a strength of character and a public spirit that were to make a lasting impression on his native town.   Marrying an heiress of great wealth, a Miss Parsley of Middlesex, and his own fortune having accumulated during his long minority to the dimensions that it had possessed before Sir Hercules had made the first of his many unsuccessful attempts to win the St. Leger, he was in a position to devote himself whole-heartedly to public life.   Entering Parliament in 1841 he represented his native town for over fifty years ; as Justice of the Peace he gained for the Drayneflete Bench an enviable reputation for unflinching severity towards the malefactor.   Three times Mayor, he was also chairman of the Drayneflete and Grand Junction Inland Navigation Co., of the Drayneflete and Southern Counties Railway Co. (until its absorption by the S.E. and Chatham, on whose board he retained a seat), and the leading supporter of the principles of Free Trade in the Drayneflete district.   A loyal Churchman of strong evangelical views, he was equally prominent in the religious and the philanthropic life, not only of the town, but of the nation.   As President of the Society for the Maintenance of the Protestant Faith he was active in initiating the prosecution of many Tractarians and Puseyites ; during his long tenure of the Chairmanship of the Society for the Evangelisation of the Hottentots he was directly responsible for the translation of the works of Isaac Watts into Bantu, Swahili, Tamil, Tanaggu and Amharic ; as founder and principal benefactor of the Fidgett Home for the Daughters of Mentally Afflicted Gentlefolk, of the Fidgett Home of Rest for Indigent School-Masters and of the Society for the Prohibition of Games of Chance, he gained a reputation that extended far beyond the confines of his native town.

In the town itself, apart from the noble statue in the Market Place, Sir Jonas is today principally commemorated by the splendid Town Hall, the work of Mr. (afterwards Sir) Giles Clerestory, R.A., of which the foundation-stone was laid by H.R.H. the Prince of Wales in 1881, and the entire cost of which the generous baronet defrayed with a characteristic munificence.   On the events of a day that was to prove ever memorable in the annals of the town a lively account is preserved in the files of the *Drayneflete Advertiser* :—

H.R.H. The Prince of Wales laying the foundation-stone of the new Town Hall in 1881. From a contemporary photograph now

Many a Drayneflete heart rejoiced this morning on looking out of the window and perceiving blue skies half hidden by a slight haze which augured well for the prospects of this auspicious day. By 10.45 a large crowd was already waiting when the Committee of Welcome arrived in a flashing cavalcade at the Railway Station. First came Lord Littlehampton, a dignified martial figure in his plumed hat and full-dress uniform of Lord Lieutenant, riding alone in an open landau behind a spanking team of the celebrated Littlehampton greys. Close behind followed His Worship the Mayor with the Town Clerk, Alderman Catchpenny and our worthy beadle, in an elegant equipage which did much credit to Messrs. Jollyboys Livery Stables. Outside the station was drawn up a Guard of Honour formed of the No. 1 Company of the Drayneflete Volunteers under the command of Major Wicker, the martial bearing and smart appearance of which was generally commended by their fellow townsmen, and the Town Band under the able direction of Mr. Register who for this occasion had exchanged the more familiar surplice of organist for the gold brandenburgs of Band-master. After the Lord Lieutenant had inspected the guard and been received by our popular station-master, Mr. Coupling, the whole party proceeded onto the No. 2 down platform which had been covered by a noble red carpet (kindly provided by Messrs. Pelmets, House Furnishings and Upholsterers, No. 3 High Street) and enlivened by large tubs of hydrangeas, the splendid appearance of which did much credit to Messrs. Mould and Puddle, Florists, No. 7 Station Road. At 11.3 precisely the Royal train drew alongside and after a slight confusion occasioned by a sudden change in the position of the Royal Saloon, His Royal Highness, looking bronzed and fit, alighted and was received by Lord Littlehampton, who introduced His Worship the Mayor, who thereupon read an address of welcome in the elegant phraseology and beautiful expression of which we fancy we detected the hand of our respected schoolmaster, Mr. Grigson. This done, His Royal Highness graciously consented to accept a bouquet from the hands of little Miss Coupling and with his usual affability insisted on shaking hands with her father, our worthy station-master.

As soon as the Royal Party appeared at the station entrance the band burst into a lively rendering of *God Save the Prince of Wales*, while cheer upon cheer broke from a thousand loyal Drayneflete throats. Having inspected the Guard of Honour, His Royal Highness entered the Lord Lieutenant's landau and, preceded by the Band, the procession moved off to the heartening strains of the Grand March from *Norma* through richly decorated streets to the Market Square.

On arrival at the site of the new Town Hall His Royal Highness was received by a Committee of Welcome consisting of Sir Jonas and Lady Fidgett, Canon Hassock, the Chief Constable and Captain Hydrant, chief of our gallant Fire Brigade whose stalwart men formed the Guard of Honour. After His Royal Highness had shaken hands with the members of the Committee and Sir Jonas had presented to him Master Jasper Fidgett, Mr. Clerestory the architect, and the foreman of the works, he received a silver trowel from the hands of the last and unhesitatingly advanced to the foundation-stone, tapping it with unerring precision in the exact centre, saying as he did so in a strong clear voice, " I deglare this stone well and truly laid ". Thereupon Canon Hassock offered up a short but beautiful prayer of his own composition and the choir accompanied by the band lifted up their voices in *Rock of Ages* in the singing of which all the company joined. It was particularly noted that His Royal Highness although not, perhaps, familiar with all the words, followed the singing with a deep and reverent attention, occasionally humming a bar or so in a light but pleasing baritone.

Note to Key on opposite page.

1. H.R.H. The Prince of Wales. 2. The Third Earl of Littlehampton. 3. Sir Jonas Fidgett, Bt. 4. Lady Fidgett. 5. Master Jasper Fidgett. 6. Colonel Wicker. 7. Canon Hassock. 8. Archdeacon Stavely-Locker. 9. His Worship the Mayor. 10. The Recorder. 11. Giles Clerestory, Esq., R.A. 12. Miss Wicker. 13. Captain Hydrant. 14. Beadle. 15. Alderman Catchpenny. 16. Mr. Smith, foreman.

Ffidget Priory.

Christmas 1907.

Left to Right. *Standing :* Sir Ephraim Kirsch, Countess Droshky, H.E. the Bavarian Ambassador, Sir Jasper Parsley-Ffidgett, Bt, Lord Spanielstown, Col. Hon. Otto Currander, and 'Bimbo'.
Seated : H.S.H. The Grandduchess Olga of Luneburg-Wolfenbüttel, Miss Shelmerdine Parsley-Ffidgett, Hon. Lady Parsley-Ffidgett, the Dowager Countess of Littlehampton.

House Party at Ffidget Priory.

The Town Hall, however, was not the only building in Drayneflete to benefit from the liberality of Sir Jonas. He it was who was the principal promoter of, and the largest subscriber to, the fund for the restoration of the parish church carried out in the 'seventies, under the supervision of Sir Gilbert Scott. The moulded plaster ceiling of eighteenth-century workmanship which had for so long concealed the beautiful open-timber roof was removed, as were also many of the fittings such as pulpit and altar-rails of the same date. In their place were substituted a beautiful new rood screen in cast bronze relieved with enamel-work, a fine stone pulpit (designed in free imitation of the baptistery of Pisa) and an exquisite reredos in carved soapstone, the work of a talented Munich designer. At the same time many of the windows, which had hitherto been plain white, were enriched with stained glass commemorating various families of the town.

On the death of Sir Jonas in 1898 he was succeeded by his only son, the youngest of a family of eleven, Jasper. Although in a way no less a public figure than his father, the fields in which the seventh baronet triumphed were rather different. Educated at Eton and Christ Church, Oxford, he inherited many of the sporting instincts of his great-grandfather, Sir Hercules, though in his case an early and persistent interest in horse-flesh was later overshadowed by enthusiasms more in keeping with the age. One of the earliest of motoring enthusiasts, his De Dion Bouton was the first automobile ever to be seen in Drayneflete and he was for many years a regular competitor in the Gordon Bennett Balloon Race. On leaving Oxford he served for a short period in the Foot Guards and subsequently as honorary attaché in Vienna ; only relinquishing the latter appointment on his marriage to Lady Consuelo Currander, the only daughter of the fifth Earl of Littlehampton. On the outbreak of the 1914 war he rejoined his regiment and served with distinction on the staff of G.H.Q. Cairo for the duration of the conflict. Such architectural changes as came about in Drayneflete in his lifetime were largely the result of commercial and municipal enterprise, and apart from adding a new wing, together with a garage, to Ffidget Priory, he was responsible for little building. Nevertheless, in the little that he did do he was careful to preserve the old-world character of his historic home and both the garage and the new wing were gabled, tile-hung

Sir Jasper Parsley-Ffidget, Bt.   From the painting by Sargent, now in the Art Gallery.

and elaborately half-timbered. Lady Consuelo Parsley-Ffidgett was a woman of great taste and keen interest in the arts and devoted all the later years of her life to making a carpet for the Great Hall in exquisite *petit-point* to a specially commissioned design by Sir Frank Brangwyn.

On the death of Sir Jasper Ffidgett in the 'twenties, at a comparatively early age (his health had long been precarious and he had

Shelmerdine, only child of Sir Jasper and Lady Parsley-Ffidget. From a painting by Modigliani, now in a private collection.

latterly spent much time in private-nursing homes), he left an only child, a daughter, Miss Shelmerdine Parsley-Ffidgett. Of astounding beauty, her début in London Society immediately after the 1914 war was long remembered, and her natural gaiety and high spirits made her a very popular member of the ' younger set '. She married, first her cousin, the eighth Lord Littlehampton (marriage dissolved 1923), second, Sophocle (' Soffie '), Duc de Vichy-Celestins (marriage dissolved 1928), third, Prince Vladimir Doppelchinsky (marriage

43

TWENTIETH-CENTURY DRAYNEFLETE

dissolved 1931), fourth, Hiram P. Hatzenbacker II of Long Island, N.Y. Her tragic death in 1935 as the result of an accident at a midnight bathing-party on the Eden Roc came as a great shock to all who knew her, the last of a family which for over five hundred years had played so prominent a part in the history of Drayneflete.

Of the many changes which have overtaken the centre of the town in the period between the wars the illustrations will speak more convincingly than any words : while the considerable suburban development on the other side of the river is of so interesting and extensive a nature that it deserves a chapter to itself.

Key to Illustration on opposite page.

Top : A. Cultural Monument scheduled under National Trust ('Poet's Corner'). B. Gasometer. C. Clover-leaf crossing and bridge. D. Communal Housing Block. E. Lunatic Asylum and Little-hampton Memorial Park. F. Cultural Monument scheduled under National Trust. G. Municipal Offices including Community Centre, Psychiatric Clinic, Crèche and Helicopter Landing-strip on the roof. H. Housing Estate for higher-income brackets. I. Communal Sports Centre, Yacht Club, and Football Ground. J. Floating Concert Hall for audience of 2,500 and full symphony orchestra. K. Power Station.

Bottom : A. Communal Housing Blocks. B. High-level Pedestrian road-bridge. C. Cultural Monument scheduled under National Trust. D. People's Restaurant, Swimming Club, Bathing Pool, Cinema and Amenities Centre. E. Underground Station.

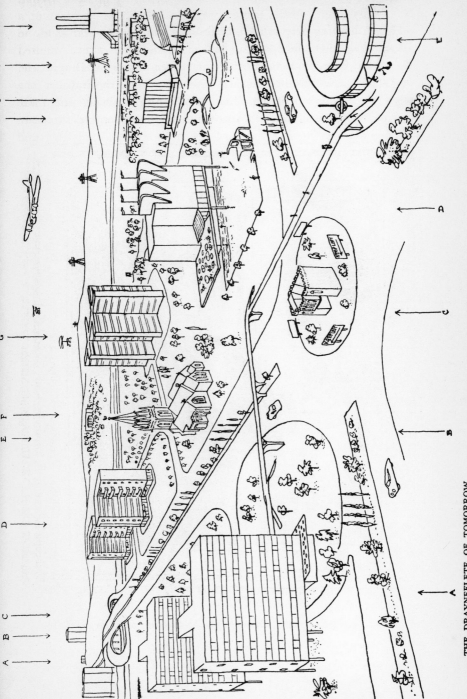

THE DRAYNEFLETE OF TOMORROW

A t the beginning of the nineteenth century the main road to the coast was practically unflanked by buildings after it crossed the river by the old bridge and a ten-minutes walk from the Market Place in this direction was sufficient to take the traveller into virgin country. A little more than a mile from the bridge there was a cross-roads at which stood a single humble inn opposite the recently

Jeremy Tipple, Esq., poet. From a portrait by Knapton, now in the Art Gallery.

48

completed walls of Lord Littlehampton's great park. The second Earl, ' Sensibility Littlehampton ' as he was known, at the time of the second rebuilding of Drayneflete Castle conceived the kindly idea of building a small Gothic Lodge at this corner of his estate for his friend and protégé, the poet Jeremy Tipple. It was the long residence of this celebrated bard in this villa which first gained for the cross-roads the appellation ' Poet's Corner ', and it was here that he wrote his immortal *The Contemplative Shepherd*, a poem of some fifteen thousand lines of which we can, alas, only quote a small selection. The passage chosen is of particular topographical interest as the landscape described is today almost entirely covered by the municipal sewage farm.

> Th'enamelled meadows that can scarce contain
> The gentle windings of the limpid Drayne
> Full oft have seen me, wandering at dawn
> As birds awaken and the startled fawn
> Leaps from her mossy bed with easy grace
> On catching sight of my indulgent face.
> Deep in some crystal pool th'enamoured trout
> Frolics and wantons up a lichened spout
> By which the stream, in many a sparkling rill,
> Is made by art to turn a water-mill.
> At last the sluggard Phoebus quits his bed
> And bares the glory of his fiery head ;
> Now all the world assumes an aspect new
> And Nature blushes neath the mantling dew.
> E'en yonder mossy walls and em'rald sward
> The home of Littlehampton's puissant lord,
> The ancient fastness of a warrior race
> Regards these marches with a kindlier face. . . .

1800

1830

By 1820 both the poet and his patron were dead. Owing to the slump at the end of the Napoleonic Wars, coupled with a bad run of luck at Crockfords, the nephew and successor of the second Earl ('Sensibility Littlehampton' had never married) had been forced to sell land for development and a row of gentlemen's villas to the design of Mr. Papworth had been erected alongside Poet's Corner, while a bailiff's cottage in the Rustic style was erected on the further side of the inn some years later. The Gothic Villa itself was now in the possession of Miss Amelia de Vere, the only child of the poet's married sister, Sophonisba, who had long kept house for her brother. Along with the house Miss Amelia had inherited much of her uncle's poetic gift, although at first this was only revealed to a small circle of intimate friends. After, however, the anonymous publication of her *Lines on the Late Massacre at Chios*, which sounded like a tocsin throughout Liberal Europe, her fame was assured. It is not, alas, possible, nor indeed is it probably necessary, to quote this celebrated work in full, but the two opening verses will serve to demonstrate both the fearless realism of the gentle poetess and her exceptional command of local colour, a command the more extraordinary in that she never, save for a brief visit to Tunbridge Wells, travelled more than ten miles from Drayneflete in all her life.

> O hark to the groans of the wounded and dying,
> Of the mother who casts a last lingering look
> At her infant aloft, understandably crying,
> Impaled on the spear of a Bashi Bazook

> O see where the vultures are patiently wheeling
> As the scimitars flash and the yataghans thud·
> On innocent victims, vainly appealing
> To dreaded Janissaries lusting for blood.

However although Miss de Vere may have never, save in imagination, set eyes on distant parts she was afforded many a complete change of scene on her own doorstep in the course of an extraordinarily

54

Miss Amelia de Vere. From a miniature by Sir George Richmond, formerly in the possession of Bill Tipple, Esq.

1860

long life. The first transformation was due to the coming of the railway. In order to save a considerable diversion and the expense of building a bridge over the Drayne, the main line kept to the south bank of the river and the station was located rather more than a mile from the centre of the town, close by Poet's Corner cross-roads, and the permanent way was carried over the coast road by viaduct. This development coincided with another of Lord Littlehampton's bad runs of luck at Baden-Baden (furthermore the noble Lord had suffered grievously by the repeal of the Corn Laws) and he took the opportunity of selling off all his property to the north of the railway.

The opening of the railway and the subsequent increase in importance of this hitherto unimportant suburb led to further rapid development. In 1855 the successful termination of the Crimean War was commemorated by the erection of a memorial fountain and the *Duke of York* public-house acquired a new façade. At the same time the increase in the congregation of the ancient church of Drayneflete Parva, half a mile up the hill, thanks to the recent completion of Gotha Terrace and other residential streets on what had previously been virgin fields, encouraged the churchwardens to add a spire to the somewhat squat tower.

At the time of Miss de Vere's death in 1890 the developments described above had been carried a stage further and the whole district was beginning to lose something of its hitherto exclusively residential character. The *Duke of York* was completely rebuilt in 1885, and four years later the Drayneflete Gas Company's Works were established alongside the railway to the south. The villas adjacent to Poet's Corner were gradually turned into shops, and the new streets which came into being at this time were largely built for the convenience of a lower grade of society.

The third Earl of Littlehampton dying at an advanced age in 1883, largely due to the shock sustained after a peculiarly bad run of luck at Homburg, was succeeded by his grandson, a man of simple tastes who divided his time between the family seat at Courantsdair and his Irish home at Spanielstown. In the Jubilee year he sold Drayneflete Castle for a lunatic asylum and presented the grounds to the Municipality as a public park.

On the death of Miss de Vere, Poet's Corner passed to her nephew,

58

The third Earl of Littlehampton in the uniform of Colonel-in-Chief of the Drayneflete Yeomanry. From an engraving after a portrait by Sir Francis Grant, P.R.A.

59

1890

Mr. Casimir De Vere-Tipple, in whom the poetic gift, so constant in this remarkable family, burnt, if not with renewed vigour, certainly with a ' hard gem-like flame '. His contributions appeared regularly

Casimir de Vere-Tipple, Esq. From a drawing by Jacques Émile Blanche. Reproduced by kind permission of the Trustees of the Tate Gallery.

in *The Yellow Book*, and were published in a slim volume by the Bodley Head under the title *Samphire and Sardonyx*. Unfortunately he did not long enjoy his property as he was forced, for private reasons, to live abroad from 1895 onwards and thenceforth resided on Capri

62

in a charming villa where his great social gifts and exquisite hospitality will still be remembered by many visitors.

After the departure of Mr. de Vere-Tipple the Poet's Corner was let on a long lease to a firm of monumental masons. A further great change in the appearance of the neighbourhood occurred when, shortly before the 1914 war, Messrs. Pinks, the drapers, entirely rebuilt their premises and a confectioner's acquired the space between them and the Poet's Corner. The secluded quiet of this once shady nook was further interrupted by the substitution of trams for horse-buses at the turn of the century, and the subsequent increase in traffic due to the coming of the internal combustion engine.

However, the poetic tradition of the locality was not even yet extinct. On his death in 1929 Mr. de Vere-Tipple left this valuable site to his favourite nephew, then at Oxford, Guillaume de Vere-Tipple, who had already made a name for himself by the publication of *Feux d'artifice* (Duckworth 1927), a collection of verse astonishing in its maturity, from which we quote a single poem, *Aeneas on the Saxophone*.

> . . . Delenda est Carthago !
> (ses bains de mer, ses plâges fleuries,
> And Dido on her lilo á sa proie attachée)

> And shall we stroll along the front
> Chatting of this and that and listening to the band ?

> The plumed and tufted sea responds
> Obliquely to the trombone's call
> The lecherous seaweed's phallic fronds
> Gently postulate the Fall.

> But between the pebble and the beach rises the doubt,
> . . . Delenda
> Between the seaside and the sea the summons,
> . . . est
> Between the *wagon* and the *lit* the implication,
> . . . Carthago.

In the years between the wars the whole character of the district was still further altered. In 1930 Messrs. Watlin acquired the *Duke of York*, which was at once rebuilt in a contemporary style which, although it at first struck those accustomed to the brassy vulgarity

1925

of the old 'pub' as strangely austere, was soon generally agreed to be both socially and aesthetically an immense improvement. Two years later another even more daring example of 'the Modern Movement', as it had come to be known, arose in the shape of the Odium

Bill Tipple. From a still from the film ' Whither Democracy ', reproduced by kind permission of the C. of I.

Cinema. While some of the more old-fashioned residents might find fault with the functional directness of this great building, nothing but praise could be accorded to the modified Georgian style in which the new Council flats across the road were built at much the same date.

The coming of a new age, of which the buildings round Poet's Corner were a portent, found a reflection in the poet's verse. Guillaume de Vere-Tipple was socially conscious to a remarkable degree and had long entertained doubts as to the security of capitalist society, doubts which received striking confirmation when International Nickel, in which he had inherited a large holding, slumped to 11½. Making a clean break with the past, his next volume of poetry, the *liftshaft* (Faber and Faber 1937) appeared above the signature Bill Tipple, and, as may be seen from the poem quoted below, this re-orientation is reflected in the contents :—

crackup in barcelona

among the bleached skeletons of the olive-trees
stirs a bitter wind
and maxi my friend from the mariahilfer strasse
importunately questions a steely sky
his eyes are two holes made by a dirty finger
in the damp blotting paper of his face
the muscular tissues stretched tautly across the scaffolding of bone
are no longer responsive to the factory siren
and never again will the glandular secretions react
to the ragtime promptings of the palais-de-danse
and I am left balanced on capricorn
the knife-edge tropic between anxiety and regret
while the racing editions are sold at the gates of football grounds
and maxi lies on a bare catalan hillside
knocked off the tram by a fascist conductor
who misinterpreted a casual glance.

The late war dealt hardly with Poet's Corner. Fortunately the house itself is still standing, but the confectioner's next door was totally demolished and extensive damage was caused to much of the surrounding property.

After the end of the conflict, in a misguided effort to relieve the considerable local housing shortage, an estate of pre-fabricated dwel-ling-houses was erected by the Borough Council in what had been erstwhile the shady groves and green retreats of the Littlehampton Memorial Park.

Today Poet's Corner is up for sale : its owner, Bill Tipple, who on the outbreak of war had been a conscientious objector, but who, on hearing the news of the invasion of Russia, experienced a complete

change of heart and immediately joined the Drayneflete section of the National Fire Service, is absent for long periods abroad in his capacity of organising secretary of the World Congress of International Poets in Defence of Peace. The long Littlehampton connection with the town is now a thing of the past ; the great race of Ffidgets is extinct. But their spirit lives on and their successors on the Borough Council are determined that the Drayneflete tradition shall at all costs be maintained. But, whatever the future may hold in store, let the visitor reflect as he goes round the Museum, as he inspects the magnificent collection of Ffidget portraits in the Art Gallery (bequeathed to the town in 1948 by the late Miss Dracula Parsley-ffigett), as he wanders in the old-world Market Place, as he paces the banks of the ' limpid Drayne ', let him reflect on the men and women who through the ages have all played their part in making Drayneflete what it is today, and see to it that we, their heirs, shall prove ourselves worthy of so goodly a heritage.

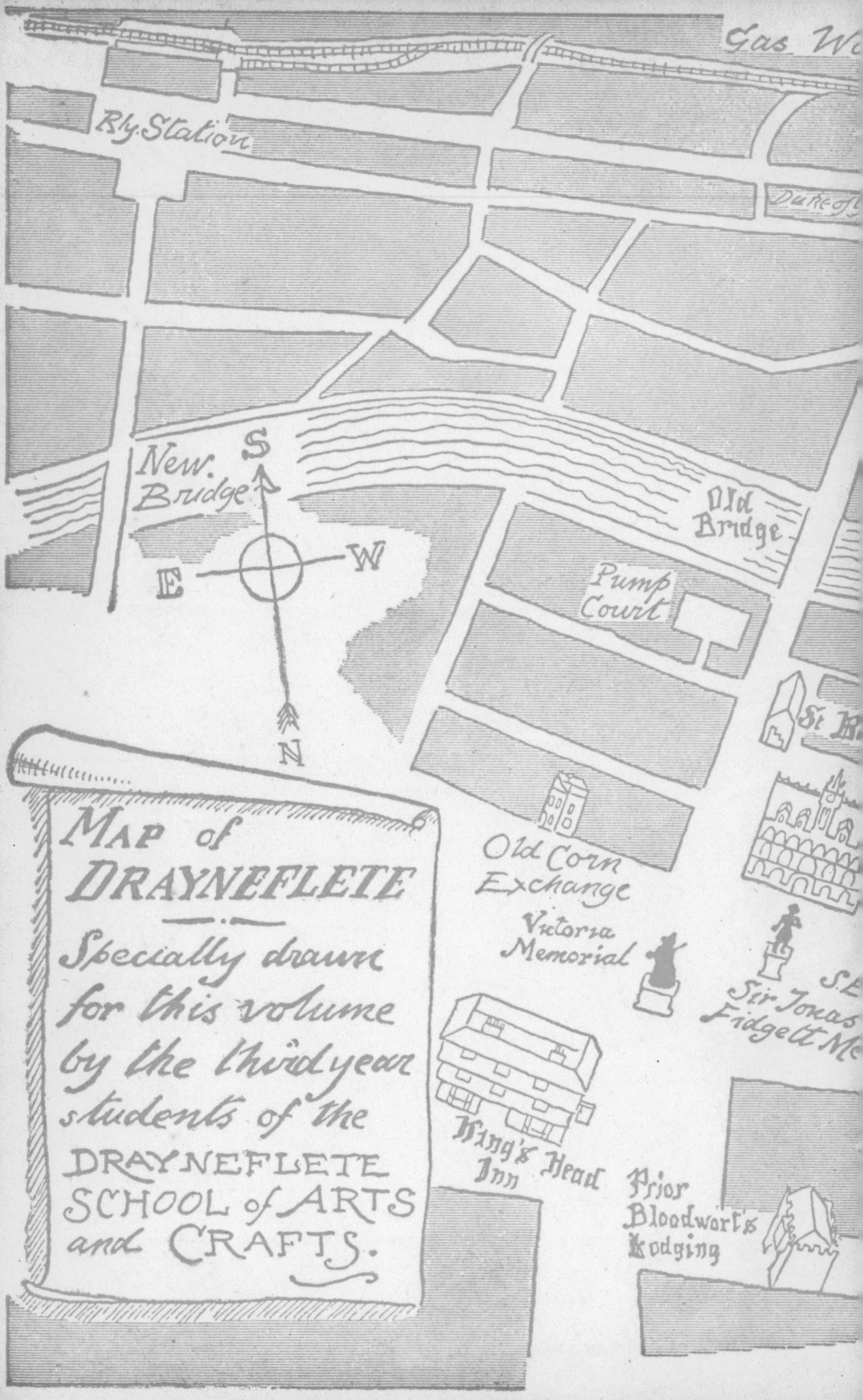

Gas W

Rly. Station

Duke St.

New. Bridge

S

E

W

N

Old Bridge

Pump Court

St K

Old Corn Exchange

Victoria Memorial

MAP of
DRAYNEFLETE

Specially drawn
for this volume
by the third year
students of the
DRAYNEFLETE
SCHOOL of ARTS
and CRAFTS.

S.L
Sir Jonas
Fidgett M

King's Head
Inn

Prior
Bloodwort's
Lodging